This book belongs to:

_____

Given by:

_____

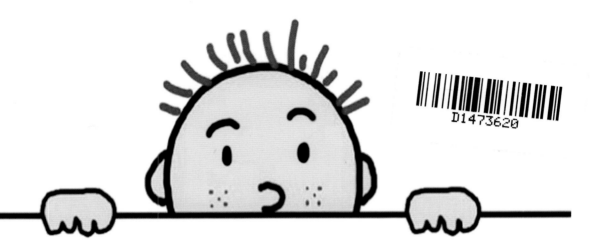

D1473620

This book is dedicated to my Family.
J.P.C.

Andy™. Andy is a registered trademark of An Andy Book Company

Library of Congress Cataloging- in- Publication Data
Library of Congress Control Number: 2007901977

ISBN-10: 0-979-38932-1 / ISBN-13: 978-0-979-38932-1   (hardcover)
ISBN-10: 0-979-38933-X / ISBN-13: 978-0-979-38933-7   (paperback)

An Andy Book Publishing
P.O. Box 116
Dyer, IN. 46311
www.AnAndyBook.com

A complete list of all of An Andy Book Titles and more information can be found at:
www.AnAndyBook.com

AN ANDY BOOK

Andy Learns to Count

1 2 3 . . .

by J.P. Curington
Author and Illustrator

1

One Ball

2

Two Balls

3

Three Balls

4

Four Balls

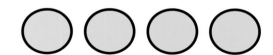

5

Five Balls

6

Six Balls

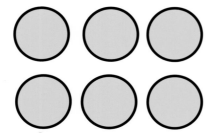

7

Seven Balls

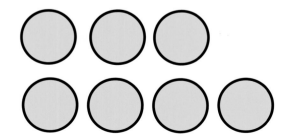

8

Eight Balls

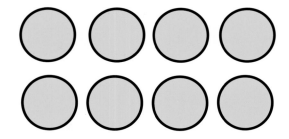

9

Nine Balls

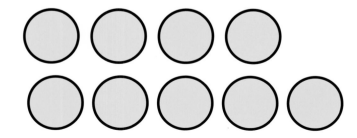

10

Ten Balls

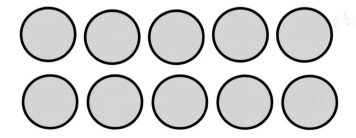

The End